en·tre·pre·neur (ahn-treh-pruh-newer):

(noun.) someone who takes risks in order to invent; to find new solutions to old problems; to discover new ways of generating income and becoming their own boss.

(proper noun.) a little girl who engages in deep thinking, deep feeling, and the inspired exploration of a big world on a journey of self-determination.

BY
CAMALO GASKIN & AUBREY GAIL FERREIRA

ILLUSTRATIONS BY ISABEL ALBERTOS

Entrepreneur Finds Her Way is available at special quantity discounts for bulk purchase for sale promotions, premiums, fundraising, and educational needs. For details, write to hello@entrepreneurthegirl.com

Text and illustration copyright © 2017

Printed in the United States of America.

Entrepreneur Finds Her Way / Ferreira, Aubrey Gail; Gaskin, Camalo
ISBN 978-0-9996967-0-5
1.Children's Literature — Fiction 2.Fantasy 3.Learning — Financial Literacy
4.Adventure and adventurers — Fiction 5.Social Justice — Fiction 6.Self-Help
7.Self-actualization 8.Learning — World Schooling 9.Entrepreneurship — Social
Entrepreneurship

First Edition

Editorial Direction & Art Direction by Aubrey Gail Ferreira & Camalo Gaskin
Illustrations and graphic design by Isabel Albertos
Contribution to Art Direction by Anette K. Hansen
Contribution to Editing by Abeer Y. Hoque

Entrepreneur The Girl
hello@entrepreneurthegirl.com
Entrepreneurthegirl.com

To Ghisele and Giacomo
for inspiring this story

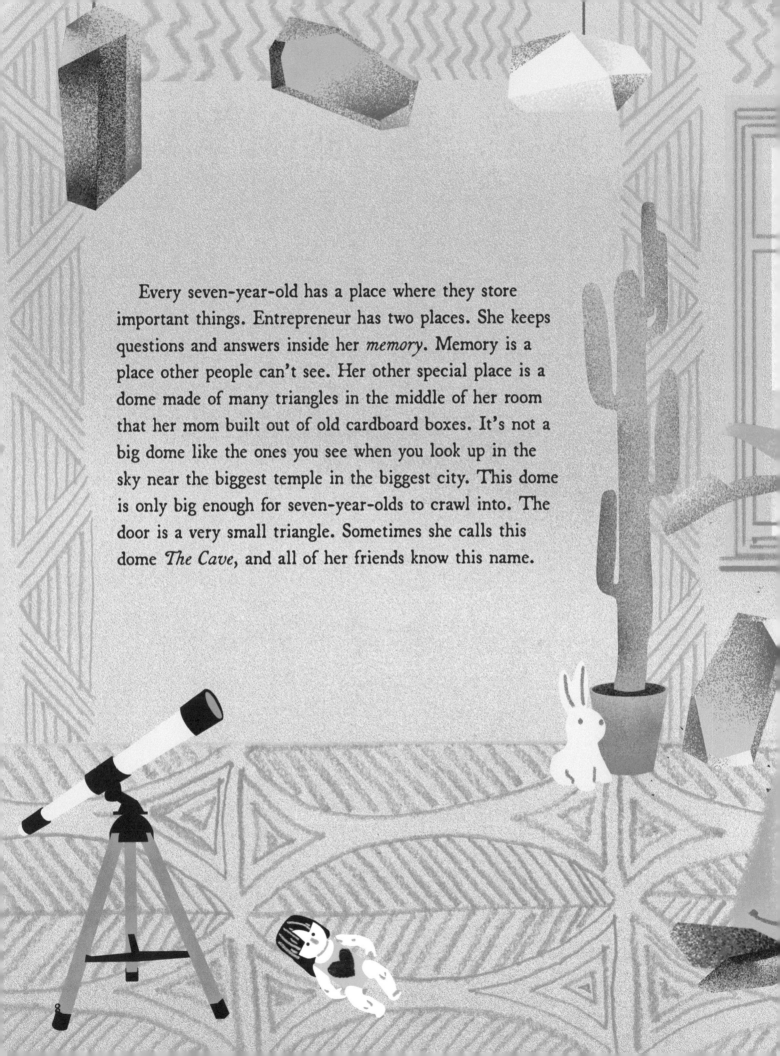

Every seven-year-old has a place where they store important things. Entrepreneur has two places. She keeps questions and answers inside her *memory*. Memory is a place other people can't see. Her other special place is a dome made of many triangles in the middle of her room that her mom built out of old cardboard boxes. It's not a big dome like the ones you see when you look up in the sky near the biggest temple in the biggest city. This dome is only big enough for seven-year-olds to crawl into. The door is a very small triangle. Sometimes she calls this dome *The Cave*, and all of her friends know this name.

Inside *The Cave*, Entrepreneur has a telescope, a Persian rug, porcelain tea cups and miniature plates, a talking chimpanzee, chalk, a drum, a friendly doll with a white beard, many baby dolls, some notebooks and pencils, a pink telephone with a rotary dial, a mini laptop computer, hollow sticks from the beach, sea shells, stones, a golden jewelry box with her baby teeth and a piece of her umbilical cord, an underwater camera, a voice recorder, and 37 keys on a ring with a flashlight and whistle. Sometimes when Entrepreneur is in *The Cave*, she talks for a long time with her important things. Even when no other kids are inside.

On this day, it's bright outside and the sun is up even after her bedtime. Entrepreneur finishes a talk in *The Cave* with her important things and crawls out. She runs through her house, because she never walks unless she's playing something grown up like Mamma or Doctor or Dog-walker or Queen.

The only other time Entrepreneur walks upright and slow is when she travels to the sun. For the journey, she pulls a tulle skirt over her head like a wig, a garbage bag around her waist like a skirt, and hooks 17 pairs of sunglasses on every part of her costume. One pair goes on her forehead and one pair goes on her eyes. Without fail, someone pulls out a camera. "Only when traveling to the sun, do I allow paparazzi," she declares. Then she walks like she's floating with her head tilted slightly back as she glides through the corridors.

13

Today Entrepreneur sprints from room to room. In the living
room, she finds her parents, whom she calls Anouk and Winfrey, and
announces that she wants to spend as much time as possible outside,
finding new important things for her cave and answering the important
questions saved in her memory. She tells Anouk and Winfrey that she
must no longer go to school.

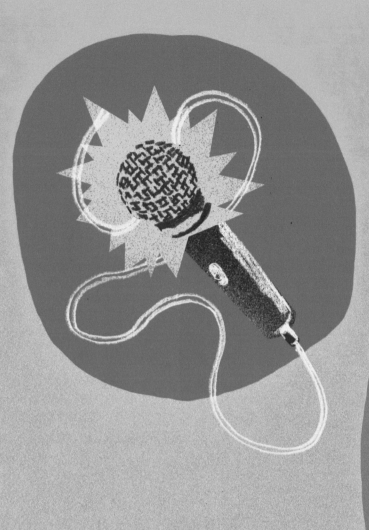

Anouk and Winfrey think about it for a very long time and eventually agree, but they propose three conditions. First, Entrepreneur will have to record everything she learns each day. Second, she will have to discover the different ways that a person earns their own money. And lastly, she has to find out what makes people happy.

When bedtime comes, Entrepreneur can't fall asleep with the *anticipation*. That's when someone is looking forward to something so very much and can't wait for it to happen.

Before the sun rises, she is dressed
with her backpack on. Anouk and Winfrey
are not even awake when she sets out the
door. Pink spills onto the sky, something
she has never seen.

There are not many people out on the streets or along the canal close to her house. In the distance, she sees buildings. Prism-light stars are staring back at her from the windows of the long buildings. People rush past. Maybe the city moves faster when the sky is pink.

20

Entrepreneur finds a spot on a platform along the canal where she can see everyone pace by. "I know how to count beyond one-thousand," she explains to her voice recorder. "One of my favorite things is to make up counting games. Counting all the people who run past with earphones in their ears will be our first game," she decides. The sky transforms to lilac, then blue. "52 runners with earphones have passed," she reports.

Now she needs a new assignment.

A runner with very short white hair stops to stretch on the platform.

"This is *serendipitous*," Entrepreneur whispers into her recorder. "That means it was not planned, but it is still a good thing." She looks up at the runner. "Why do you run, Runner Woman?" she asks.

The runner smiles at her, "I run because it makes me feel good."

"It makes you happy?" Entrepreneur asks.

"Yes," says the runner, "and it makes me think of good ideas."

"How does running make you have good ideas?" asks Entrepreneur.

"Well," says the runner, "When I run, I feel that my mind is getting bigger and bigger. With every breath I take, something inside me grows. Every time I want to stop but keep going, it doubles in size. It feels like a giant ocean."

"Wow," says Entrepreneur.

"Yes... and when my ocean gets very, very large, big fish can swim around inside which wouldn't be able to fit in a tiny ocean. The fish are my good ideas."

Entrepreneur beams, "I have a memory where I keep the important things I learn. The more I learn, the bigger my memory gets so it can fit all the important things!"

The runner laughs and says, "Yes, it's a lot like that. I have been running for so many years, which means I have a very big and very deep ocean."

Entrepreneur imagines the runner's ocean of ideas. She says, "So you must have a lot of fish."

"Indeed. Fish, sea kelp, and jellyfish too." the runner says, "They are all much bigger than they used to be and there are so many more of them! Sometimes when I least expect it, a humpback whale swims in. Those are my great and wonderful ideas."

Entrepreneur is very curious. "Tell me, Runner Woman, what was your great humpback whale idea?" she asked.

The runner smiles big. "My great idea was to start a marathon in 100 cities," she says.

Entrepreneur's eyes open wide. She imagines all the big fish in the giant deep oceans in the minds of every runner. She imagines funny-shaped ideas and scary ideas, cute ideas and magnificent ideas. Suddenly she wants to run.

"Runner Woman," Entrepreneur says, "Can I come with you today and try to do what you do?"

"I would like that very much," says the runner. "Stretch with me for a moment and then we will run."

So Entrepreneur begins to imitate the runner. She feels her muscles stretching one by one. It hurts a little bit, but in a way that also feels

good. This is surprising and exciting. She has never felt a hurt that also feels good before this very moment.

"Now," the runner says, "I have a lot of practice doing this so I plan to run very far. You are free to stop whenever you like and wave goodbye. I will keep going, but I will always remember this day and the wonderful questions you asked me."

"Okay, wonderful," Entrepreneur says laughing, and she cinches up the straps of her backpack so it's tight and steady on her back. The two, one big and one little, take off running at a slow and steady pace.

As Entrepreneur pumps her legs, she can feel
her breath changing and her heart beating harder
and faster. This is fun, she thinks. The wind blowing on her
face and through her hair feels nice. Suddenly she remembers
the questions she promised her parents she would ask.

"How do you get the money," she asks, "for your great and
wonderful idea?"

"Good question," says the runner. "It costs money to start
a marathon in 100 cities and it also costs money for me to
support myself. You know: food, shelter, water, heat, internet.
All the basic necessities." The runner laughs and although
Entrepreneur doesn't really know why, she laughs too.
Running makes her feel big and excited.

The runner continues, "To get the money that I need

to live and to organize my projects, I partner with big companies."

Entrepreneur is puzzled. "I know that a partner is when two people work together on the same project. I didn't know that a company could be a partner too."

"They can—you have the right idea. If a company likes your project and thinks it'll be good for them too, they will work with you to help make it happen. It's sometimes called a *sponsorship*—when a company sponsors your idea," says the runner.

"Ah," Entrepreneur says, "So, companies sponsor your marathons and that means they give you money to help you make it happen."

"That's right," says the runner.

"And what about your living money? Do they sponsorship that too?"

"Yes, I earn my living money through the sponsorship as well," says the runner.

"And what does the company get in return?" Entrepreneur asks.

"Another great question. Well, usually they want to put their names on big signs at the marathons to tell people about their company. That's why I only work with companies that I really like. Companies that do some good in the world. I like helping them and they like helping me. We come together to organize a marathon. And then, do you know what happens next? The marathon makes money and we donate it to a good cause!"

"What's a *cause*?" Entrepreneur asks.

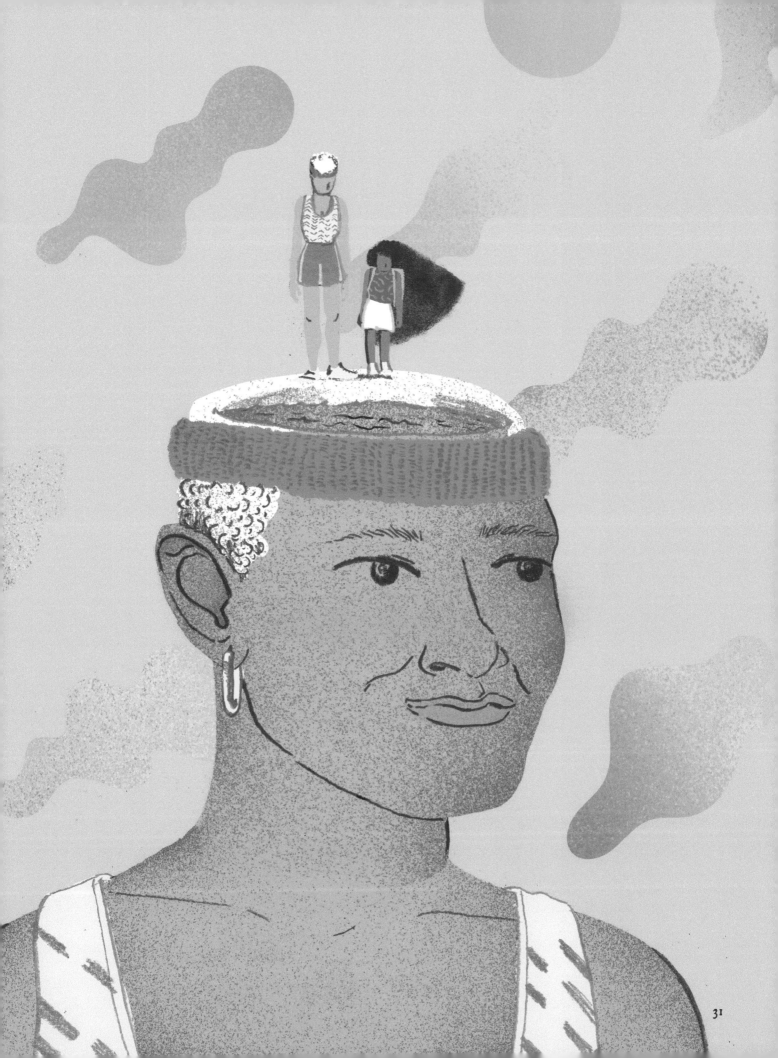

"Sometimes things happen in this world that break your heart. Let's say there's a big earthquake that destroys people's houses and injures people. We can donate the marathon money to help rebuild houses and take care of the people who got hurt."

"That would be a very good cause," Entrepreneur says.

"Can you think of a cause that you would donate marathon money to?" asks the runner.

"Yes!" Entrepreneur thinks of one right away. Maybe it's because she's running but her ideas seem bigger and clearer. "A boy joined my school last summer who had to leave his country in a boat. A *war* came and turned his house to dust. A war is when people fight with machines and words and everything turns to dust. Sometimes, it makes children

have no parents. And that hurts my heart."

"Oh, that hurts my heart too," says the runner.

"I would give the money to him and other people like him from his country whose houses turned to dust so they could find new houses to live in. No one can live in dust." Entrepreneur says.

"Now that is a great cause if I ever heard one," says the runner. "You know, you could start your own marathon and raise money for your wonderful cause."

Entrepreneur imagines what this might look like. The two continue to run, putting one foot down in front of the next in a slow and steady pace. As she huffs and puffs, she begins to dream. Suddenly, Entrepreneur meets her ocean.

She's running but she is also diving deep into a big blue sea. Fish swim by with numbers on their backs. They are racing. Their fins are rainbow-colored and *iridescent*, reflecting the sun in a beautiful and glittery way. These are all the different people she could meet, each with their own ocean of ideas, each of them running and dreaming.

Her school friend whose house turned to dust is suddenly with her. They hug tight and gaze through his scuba mask. They are both filled with hope. His mask fills up with tears, yet he is smiling with excitement. They flip and curl around in the deep blue ocean together. A pair of white sunglasses floats by. Seaweed tickles their toes and they stretch their fingers upward into a warm stripe of sunlight.

Entrepreneur stops running and rubs her eyes. She takes deep breaths of crisp cool air into her belly until her breath and heartbeat slow. Her heart feels full of peace.

When she opens her eyes, the runner woman is far ahead, too far to call out to. But when Entrepreneur whispers, "Thank you," the runner woman looks back, winks, and continues on her way.

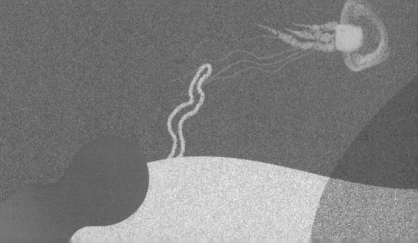

Entrepreneur walks back home and climbs the steps to the door of her building. Standing there, with her hand on the doorknob, she looks around and sees something very special. On one side of the house, the sun is setting, and on the other side, half of the moon is shining. She smiles and breathes in deep.

"We are very close, but very far. So many new little fish everywhere," she says before turning off her recorder. She runs inside to find Anouk and Winfrey. It's nearly bedtime and she has a lot to share.

After telling Anouk and Winfrey her stories, Entrepreneur sprawls out on the floor of her room with all the impressions of the day filling the air. Her muscles feel wobbly from all the running. She closes her eyes. She's tired, but ideas are still moving through her mind—some slow, some fast.

She whispers to the recorder in her hand, "I love my house. I love having my own room full of important things. Everyone probably does. Even my friend from school and all the people from his country. They all had to leave on boats, but what if they could have new houses? My wish would be to find a company to help me organize a marathon so that these families can have new homes."

Entrepreneur has a mouse minute. This means that she is very quiet and makes no noise for one minute. Then, she springs up quickly and grabs her recorder again. "Ah, I have a big idea," she whispers excitedly into her recorder. "The woman with the black turtleneck and funny white glasses who I met on my class trip to the Bauhaus Museum for buildings! She showed us films and photos and models about how to make houses from any material—even plants, or Tyvex, or wood, or glass, or mushrooms, or even straw and mud."

"Making mud houses was so much fun and very messy. I like messy. I think the turtleneck woman can make real houses too. For people to actually live inside. She told us that she's an *architect*. Architects draw and build houses. She told us that she works in the museum on some days and in a *firm* on the other days. The firm is her company where she works with her architect friends to design and build buildings together."

Entrepreneur picks up a little bag in the corner of her room. Inside is a little square card with writing on it and some popsicle sticks. "The woman gave us this card," she tells the recorder, "and told us that we could come back to visit her whenever we wanted to talk about buildings." Entrepreneur is very sleepy, but she feels her idea growing. "I can ask her my questions. She knows all about buildings. She would know all the firms and museums that would like to help us with the marathon to raise money for new homes."

Entrepreneur is very satisfied with her memory.
She takes another mouse minute, and smiles a very
sleepy smile. She wraps her arms around her body and
rolls over to her bed. Anouk and Winfrey's footsteps
approach her room. She wants to talk with them again,
but she's just too tired. She slowly closes her eyes
as she whispers, "This idea must be a dolphin idea,
because it's springing up and diving deep. It makes me
very happy."

And with that last thought, Entrepreneur pulls up
her blanket and sinks into a deep sleep.

Good night. Dream big.

Camalo Gaskin is a speaker, mother, and advocate for social and healthcare models that honor self-determination for women, girls and people who bend gender norms. Founder of *Birth to Birth*, an acclaimed international symposium series, she uses ritual and storytelling to integrate evidence-based practices with sensory play.

Aubrey Gail Ferreira is a published poet and interdisciplinary artist. She is an acclaimed educator for creative writing and dance, where she develops innovative curriculum on multi-media platforms for all ages, radically engaging the full spectrum of learners' senses and abilities.

CPSIA information can be obtained
at www.ICGtesting.com
Printed in the USA
LVHW071153180319
611003LV00017B/535/P